Right at the very edge of the world, just where the sea seems to begin, there is a tiny island called Mauritius.

It is emerald green and, wherever you go when you're there, mountains stand like giants just behind you, watching over you. Mauritius is the land of the dodo, that huge big bird that doesn't even know how to fly. I love dodos, so I'm going to go and find them.

But how on earth can I find even one single dodo?

I set off to look for a dodo. I take a long, straight track between two big sugar cane fields.

All of a sudden, a baby mongoose peeps out at me in the distance. I move closer. But.. wheeee! It just shoots off across the path and vanishes into thin air, its tail following after.

A bit further on, I find myself right in the middle of a forest of giant fan trees. Wanderers' palms. There, a whole family of monkeys come and surprise me. Two of them stop and stare at me, and then pull funny faces. I ask them where I might possibly find a dodo, even just one, but they take absolutely no notice of me.

But, where on earth can I find a dodo?

In the village, I saw beautiful women going past in their long, brightly coloured sarees, brought all the way from India.

In one street, children were all coming out of school: their ancestors are from all the countries and all the religions of the world but, being in school uniform, they all look much the same. The girls are in the same skirts, the boys in the same trousers. Very practical to get dressed in the morning.

As they stroll along in groups, they are all eating jambloons, which are making their lips go bright purple.

But, where on earth can I find a dodo?

Wandering along, I suddenly come across the most beautiful little cove, where the lagoon is so warm that I just dive straight in. I go right under the water.

When I open my eyes, I see all sorts of brightly coloured coral. One piece is the shape of a little tree made of lace. Another one is a big ball, just like a cauliflower.

I see fish disguised as Red Indians and even a trumpet-fish with a long snout. On the sand I see a star-fish, the size of my hand, its five fingers pulsing in the swells.

As I am getting out of the water, I nearly tread on a horrible jelly-like thing. Yuck! But it's only a sea-cucumber: although it is very ugly, it is completely harmless.

It does nothing but laze around all day.

Later I look up into a big tree and see a bright yellow canary, perched on a branch. It is keeping an eye on me.

So, I throw a few bread crumbs on to the ground for it, but three fierce bulbuls, each with its smart black hat on, just fly down and gobble up all the bread crumbs.

So, I throw another handful for my friend, the canary, but this time bossy mynahs swoop down and eat them all up.

All the while, a baby chameleon lies almost invisible on a branch, just watching. Completely still.
Chameleons wouldn't dream of getting mixed up in some bird fight.
The canary gives up and flies away home.
Life isn't easy when you're so little.

Oh, dear! I am getting rather hungry myself, come to think of it.

Here, all year round, pawpaws just hang high up in their trees, coming straight out of the trunks, waiting to be picked.

What I would really like is a big, juicy mango. When I bite into it, juice will run all the way down my chin.

Or, what about a custard apple, all white, creamy and sweet? Or a star fruit, that I can slice into bright yellow stars? Or maybe I could pick a granadilla? When its skin goes all wrinkled, that's when it's best!

But, where on earth can I find a dodo?

In my bedroom, there are two geckoes on the wall. They are almost transparent.

Each one makes a loud "tcheeck-tcheeck" sound at the other one. Then they lie in wait for mosquitoes. Look how easily they stay up there! It must be those little suction pads they've got on the soles of their feet. I like them, the geckoes. But I hate the big flying cockroaches that sometimes dive in.

Suddenly, a little frog jumps right into the house. It must have lost its way. It usually stays next to the pond with its friends. At night, they make a terrible racket, croaking away like a bad choir. But if I go out to visit them, they all just shut right up. Shhh! Then, as soon as I move away, there they go again, croak! croak! croak!

This morning, I went to the Pamplemousses Gardens. There I saw water lilies with leaves as big as giant pie-dishes. And I saw funny little 'bottle-palms' trees with great pot-bellied trunks. And there's a huge screen of giant bamboo, brought all the way from China. There is a tree that has a bark that gives off a beautiful camphor smell.   See how it cleared my nose! But what I like best is   the banyan-tree:

I love the way its long strands trail right down to the ground. If you grab hold of a big plaited strand and hold on really tight, you can take a run and a jump, and swing up into the air, laughing as you go!

In Dodoland, there are flowers all the year round.

Some have strange names meaning "crab pincers" or "cat's tail". There are even vieilles filles meaning "spinsters", which are quite prickly flowers. Of course, they don't mix with vieux garçons, meaning "bachelors". I love the birds of paradise: their flowers are so tall and straight, with brightly coloured wings that never will fly.

At nightfall, I harvest a basketful of frangipani flowers.
Their perfume is the sweetest of all.

But, where on earth
can I find a dodo?

In the market, merchants sell prawn-crackers, savoury pancakes called dhal purees and other snacks with very special names: pootoo, moutaye, ladoo, coconut macatchias.

But what I like best of all is calamindas, candy floss that sticks to my nose when I eat it off the stick.

Afterwards, I get so thirsty I have a good excuse to drink a tall glass of alouda. Alouda is a cool, milk-shake drink with diced jelly in it, and also with seeds called toc maria floating in it. They swell up when they are soaked in milk.

I search everywhere for a dodo. In The Vale, Cottage and Long Mountain. I even look in Trou-aux-Biches, which means Doe Valley, but I still don't find a single dodo. I don't see a doe either, for that matter.

When I search Ile aux Cerfs, which means Deer Island, I don't see any sign of a dodo there either. Nor do I see a deer, for that matter. So, I go to a village called Deux Frères, which means Two Brothers, and to another one called Quatre Soeurs, which means Four Sisters, but still no dodo. Nor brothers or sisters, for that matter.

Finally I go and look for a dodo in Rivière des Anguilles, which means Eel Creek, and there I see a host of crocodiles taking their afternoon nap. I make sure not to disturb them. Their teeth are all bared: long and razor-sharp.

But, where on earth can I find a dodo?

Oh, dear. No dodo. I sit down on the beach at Pomponette.

Then, as a cloud goes by high up in the sky, I lie down on the white sand and just listen to the sea as it splashes and gurgles against the rocks in the distance. When the sea is angry like the sea at Pomponette, you should never disturb it either.

A couple of tourists are walking along the beach. You can see that they are tourists because they wear loud shirts with big floral patterns on them.

The fishermen set out in their boats at crack of dawn here. They know the sea, they do. They even know the art of talking to the waves.

Still no dodo.

I wrack my brains until finally I come to the conclusion that if I can't find dodos anywhere at all, it is probably because they don't want me to find them.

Maybe human beings didn't treat them that well in the past.

Maybe they prefer to go and hide in real Dodoland.

No sooner does that thought cross my mind, than I feel my eyes closing. I dream I am going to join them in their little plot of Dodoland right at the very edge of the world where the sea seems to begin.

In the same series:

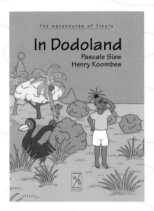

In Dodoland
Pascale Siew
Henry Koombes

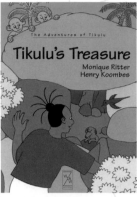

The Adventures of Tikulu
Tikulu's Treasure
Monique Ritter
Henry Koombes

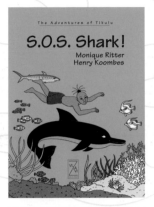

The Adventures of Tikulu
S.O.S. Shark!
Monique Ritter
Henry Koombes

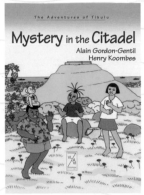

The Adventures of Tikulu
Mystery in the Citadel
Alain Gordon-Gentil
Henry Koombes

Meli-melo in the Molasses
Alain Gordon-Gentil
Henry Koombes

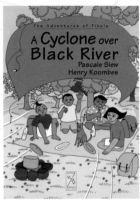

The Adventures of Tikulu
A Cyclone over Black River
Pascale Siew
Henry Koombes

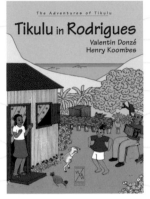

The Adventures of Tikulu
Tikulu in Rodrigues
Valentin Donzé
Henry Koombes

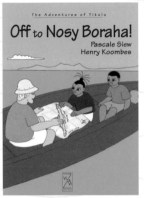

The Adventures of Tikulu
Off to Nosy Boraha!
Pascale Siew
Henry Koombes

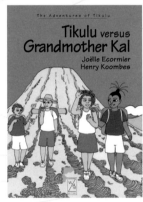

The Adventures of Tikulu
Tikulu versus Grandmother Kal
Joëlle Ecormier
Henry Koombes

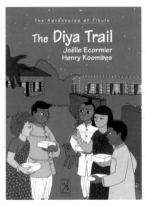

The Adventures of Tikulu
The Diya Trail
Joëlle Ecormier
Henry Koombes

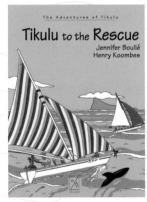

The Adventures of Tikulu
Tikulu to the Rescue
Jennifer Boullé
Henry Koombes

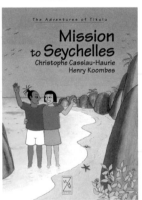

The Adventures of Tikulu
Mission to Seychelles
Christophe Cassiau-Haurie
Henry Koombes

The Adventures of Tikulu
Tikulu in India
Pascale Siew
Henry Koombes

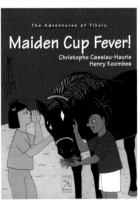

The Adventures of Tikulu
Maiden Cup Fever!
Christophe Cassiau-Haurie
Henry Koombes

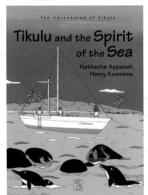

The Adventures of Tikulu
Tikulu and the Spirit of the Sea
Nathacha Appanah
Henry Koombes

Glossary:
. Pootoo / putu: Steamed rice pudding decorated with coconut gratings
. Moutaye / mutay: Squiggle-shaped dessert with a very sweet filling
. Ladoo / ladu: Very rich rounded balls made with chick peas flour, almonds and sugar
. Macatia coco: Small coconut bun